<u>Handwriting is part of Primary English whether they like it or not</u>

'<u>Handwriting Heaven or Handwriting Hell</u>' works by setting clear targets.
We think kids do better if they know exactly what they're being asked to do...

> **BY THE END OF THE YEAR YOU HAVE TO WRITE <u>EVERYTHING</u> IN A JOINED UP STYLE, USING CONSISTENT AND APPROPRIATE JOINING LINES THAT JOIN <u>CONSISTENTLY</u> SIZED LETTERS.**

...and this book gives kids lots of <u>practice</u> to <u>make sure they do</u>.

<u>Here's how it works...</u>

1) Make sure the whole class knows that:
   - the point of this book is to GET INTO HANDWRITING HEAVEN
   - you stay in Heaven by <u>meeting targets</u>
   - to do well in primary English you must <u>write everything in a joined up style</u>.

2) We've left a space for you to write a target at the top of each page, eg. 5/20.

3) Targets should get <u>tougher</u> over the year.

4) If a child meets their target, they're in Handwriting Heaven, but if they miss one they go to Handwriting Hell — until next time they meet their targets.

5) Then you can circle the Heaven or Hell at the top of each page.

6) Even better, make a massive poster, with stickers for the kids' names. Move the names from Hell to Heaven in a weekly ceremony. Give prizes for going to Heaven, and punishments for going to Hell — may we suggest running round the school waving their hands in the air shouting, "I hate rice pudding! I hate rice pudding!" *

* Because, as everyone knows, in Handwriting Hell they make you eat cold rice pudding, wearing a balaclava and only one sock.

Joining the letter 'a'

In order to reach Handwriting Heaven, make sure that in ☐ out of 20 of the sentences below, the letter 'a' is written and joined correctly.

1) In Alabama they have a lot of alarm clocks.

2) Samantha sang to her sad father.

3) Paul was angry with the naughty alligator.

4) I hate football but I love playing netball.

5) It's because I can't tackle, but I can catch!

6) Alan made a batch of tomato cakes.

7) I'd like to swap my cap for a larger hat.

8) As the play ended, the audience all clapped.

9) Except for my gran, who'd fallen asleep.

10) Dave said it was unfair that he came last.

11) I'm amazed at how fast I trapped the badger.

12) He packed his bags and caught the train.

13) He's headed for Australia, but he'll be back.

14) I can balance many apples on my head.

15) Laura watched the bad cat catch carrots.

16) Anyone can laugh at any time of day.

17) Jane stands on the wall and seems taller.

18) My garden is beautiful but my wife is fat.

19) Amanda's carpet is great to dance on.

20) The giraffe walked fast past the parked cars.

Now practise your letter 'a', by writing out this passage below

Handwriting Heaven is amazing, it's great.
And as for Punctuation Paradise — I can hardly wait.

Joining the letter 'a'

a ....

a ....

1) ....

2) ....

3) ....

4) ....

5) ....

6) ....

7) ....

8) ....

9) ....

10) ....

11) ....

12) ....

13) ....

14) ....

15) ....

16) ....

17) ....

18) ....

19) ....

20) ....

Paragraph practice

....

....

Joining the letter 'b'

In order to reach Handwriting Heaven, make sure that in ☐ out of 20 of the sentences below, the letter 'b' is written and joined correctly.

1) Barmy Bobby thinks birthdays are boring.

2) Beware of the bursting bubbles.

3) My buttons are blue but my belt is black.

4) The bee buzzed and flew off backwards.

5) The badly behaved goat butted my behind.

6) My brothers are brave, but I am brainy.

7) The morning was bright and beautiful.

8) My dad likes beer, but I like strawberries.

9) My beloved monkey was beaming with pride.

10) He'd been the best in the beauty contest.

11) So Becky bought him a bunch of bananas.

12) Babies were bouncing all over the balcony.

13) My rabbit is brown and she nibbles my boots.

14) Bridget is bigger and bolder than Barney.

15) It's because she's a bear, and he is a beetle.

16) I can't believe I've broken my blender.

17) The best boys are those who wear braces.

18) My thumb was bleeding — my bunny bit it!

19) I put on a bandage and felt much better.

20) My friend Brian's book about boats is brilliant.

Now practise your letter 'b', by writing out this passage below

"You're brilliantly brainy," said my teacher to me,

"You'll be in Handwriting Heaven in time for your tea."

Joining the letter 'b'

b ....

b ....

1) ....

2) ....

3) ....

4) ....

5) ....

6) ....

7) ....

8) ....

9) ....

10) ....

11) ....

12) ....

13) ....

14) ....

15) ....

16) ....

17) ....

18) ....

19) ....

20) ....

Paragraph practice

....

....

Joining the letter 'c'

In order to reach Handwriting Heaven, make sure that in ☐ out of 20 of the sentences below, the letter 'c' is written and joined correctly.

1) Catching cold in winter is a piece of cake!

2) The clever cow clearly belongs in college.

3) Cam climbed on his pony and cantered away.

4) My cosy cottage is never clean.

5) The bacon was crispy but rather cold.

6) Claire kicked the ticking clock and chuckled.

7) I can't stand cheeky cats who call me names.

8) The clown's clothes were crimson.

9) Chris couldn't come to count my cucumbers.

10) Carol was caught cursing at the top of a cliff.

11) I was feeling cheerful until I cut my face.

12) I caught it on a branch while chasing Chloe.

13) Cheerleaders can chant and do cartwheels.

14) My crazy cousin made a cactus crumble.

15) Chickens calm down after eating custard.

16) The cute chipmunk crunched up a carrot.

17) He complained when I climbed the curtains.

18) I couldn't complain — I was caught in the act.

19) The crowd marched across the icy coast.

20) Cottage cheese and coleslaw's a tasty snack.

Now practise your letter 'c', by writing out this passage below

Cheer up, it takes time to catch on with this stuff,
So practise and practise til you've learned enough.

Joining the letter 'c'

c ....

c ....

1) ....

2) ....

3) ....

4) ....

5) ....

6) ....

7) ....

8) ....

9) ....

10) ....

11) ....

12) ....

13) ....

14) ....

15) ....

16) ....

17) ....

18) ....

19) ....

20) ....

Paragraph practice

....

....

Joining the letter 'd'

In order to reach Handwriting Heaven, make sure that in ▢ out of 20 of the sentences below, the letter 'd' is written and joined correctly.

1) Don't drag that donkey through my doorway.

2) The dark dungeon was dismal and dreary.

3) Duncan was delighted to dry the dishes.

4) Debbie's dancing was dreadful.

5) Mr Andrews doodled all over my drawing.

6) I asked if it was him and he didn't deny it.

7) Then he decided to destroy the evidence.

8) I saved it just as he was feeding it to my dog.

9) Dad couldn't find his diamond hairband.

10) I'd hidden it where it would never be found!

11) The daffodils looked dirty so I washed them.

12) I donated my designer denim handbag.

13) Most dragons find doughnuts delicious.

14) I don't like the dark much but I'm not scared.

15) Sudden sounds drive Derek round the bend.

16) I was determined to dive into the deep end.

17) We buried my dad in the sand at the seaside.

18) The daft panda stood on his head.

19) Donald described his daring deeds.

20) The duck waddled towards the pond.

Now practise your letter 'd', by writing out this passage below

Don't be daunted, don't despair,

Handwriting Heaven — you're almost there.

Joining the letter 'd'

d ....

d ....

1) ....

2) ....

3) ....

4) ....

5) ....

6) ....

7) ....

8) ....

9) ....

10) ....

11) ....

12) ....

13) ....

14) ....

15) ....

16) ....

17) ....

18) ....

19) ....

20) ....

Paragraph practice

....

....

Joining the letter 'e'

In order to reach Handwriting Heaven, make sure that in ☐ out of 20 of the sentences below, the letter 'e' is written and joined correctly.

1) Elephants are clever — they never forget.

2) I sowed seeds to grow peas and beans.

3) My feet grew to be eleven metres long!

4) Ellen the mermaid lives in the deep blue sea.

5) She is friends with fishes and eats seaweed.

6) I need to see sheep for meetings every week.

7) If my bees sleep too much — I get no honey.

8) Peter loves beetroot for breakfast, and tea!

9) The cheeky mouse sneered at the feeble cat.

10) "It's not easy being green!" cried the newt.

11) Never drop litter — it hurts my feelings.

12) I love playing hide and seek with my pet deer.

13) It's hard to believe my sister's only three.

14) She sees and hears everything I do!

15) My niece made nineteen pies yesterday.

16) I feed my kitten cheese to keep away fleas.

17) Chelsea and Everton both play in blue.

18) I like to be clean, but sometimes I'm smelly.

19) All these sentences are making me sleepy.

20) I'll keep myself awake with lots of coffee.

Now practise your letter 'e', by writing out this passage below

For Handwriting Heaven, remember this line —
Practice makes perfect, every time.

Joining the letter 'e'

e ....

e ....

1) ....

2) ....

3) ....

4) ....

5) ....

6) ....

7) ....

8) ....

9) ....

10) ....

11) ....

12) ....

13) ....

14) ....

15) ....

16) ....

17) ....

18) ....

19) ....

20) ....

Paragraph practice

....

....

Joining the letter 'f'

In order to reach Handwriting Heaven, make sure that in ☐ out of 20 of the sentences below, the letter 'f' is written and joined correctly.

1) My favourite friends are famous and French.

2) Fiona has a fantastic gift for making trifle.

3) I was huffing and puffing as I climbed the cliff.

4) The faithful fox came back to find me.

5) Fire-breathing dragons make fearsome foes.

6) The parrot's feathers were fabulous colours.

7) My cat is called Jeff — he's very fluffy.

8) He loves playing football, and fighting.

9) My friend Stef's favourite food is toffee.

10) The first footballer ran onto the field.

11) Farmer Fred keeps cows and ducks and stuff.

12) Fifi won a fortune, and now she's filthy rich!

13) My T.V. is far too old — it flickers and fades.

14) In the future I'd like to live in Africa or further.

15) My fish flipped and fell onto the floor.

16) I'd love to go on safari and see a giraffe.

17) Asif favours playing football and frisbee.

18) But Raif, who's fifteen, prefers fencing.

19) "Turn that music off," fumed my father.

20) I found a frog in our loft feeding on fudge.

Now practise your letter 'f', by writing out this passage below

Handwriting Heaven is fantastic and fun,

So please don't be daft, just get your practice done.

Joining the letter 'f'

f ....

f ....

1) ....

2) ....

3) ....

4) ....

5) ....

6) ....

7) ....

8) ....

9) ....

10) ....

11) ....

12) ....

13) ....

14) ....

15) ....

16) ....

17) ....

18) ....

19) ....

20) ....

Paragraph practice

....

....

Joining the letter 'g'

In order to reach Handwriting Heaven, make sure that in ☐ out of 20 of the sentences below, the letter 'g' is written and joined correctly.

1) The greengrocer's garage is full of garbage.

2) My grandma's called Aggie and she's great!

3) I saw a gigantic slug in the garden — ugh!

4) Frogs are green and my bangles are golden.

5) The garden gate swung shut with a bang.

6) I love singing and my dog loves digging.

7) If you get gangrene in your leg it might fall off.

8) My brother Greg is a ghastly sight — gross!

9) But his girlfriend Maggie says he's gorgeous.

10) The mighty stag galloped across the grass.

11) Greenhouses are good for growing things.

12) My grandad is grateful for a glass of lager.

13) Douglas is a gnome and he's not very big.

14) He wears baggy clothes and has bandy legs!

15) He plays golf a lot, and rides an iguana.

16) I begged to go out running with my Gran.

17) The ugly old hag looked gleefully at her gold.

18) I've got a bag full of grimy, soggy socks!

19) The silly girls never stopped giggling.

20) I can play the guitar and we'll sing together.

Now practise your letter 'g', by writing out this passage below

Handwriting Hell is so gloomy and grim,

And if you don't practise, you'll have to go in.

Joining the letter 'g'

g ....

g ....

1) ....

2) ....

3) ....

4) ....

5) ....

6) ....

7) ....

8) ....

9) ....

10) ....

11) ....

12) ....

13) ....

14) ....

15) ....

16) ....

17) ....

18) ....

19) ....

20) ....

Paragraph practice

....

....

Joining the letter 'h'

In order to reach Handwriting Heaven, make sure that in ⬚ out of 20 of the sentences below, the letter 'h' is written and joined correctly.

1) I'd hide from a hippo if he was hungry.

2) Even though he probably wouldn't harm me.

3) My chum Hugh thinks he's a hero.

4) I think he's too hairy to be handsome.

5) I chuckled as I ate my chips with chopsticks.

6) Sheep can be short-tempered in heatwaves.

7) Kathy's hair is short and she hopes to grow it.

8) Sharon's was long but she had it chopped off.

9) I hate being too hot, but it's horrid being chilly.

10) Charley cheated at hopscotch.

11) Natasha thinks her homework is horrible.

12) She shouldn't fret as her teacher can help.

13) The happy hyenas lived high in the hills.

14) Helen had hoped her hat would be cheaper.

15) Playing hopscotch with chickens is hopeless!

16) Everyone cheered for the new champions.

17) I lost my new hamster down a hole.

18) But he came back home when he got hungry.

19) The chimpanzee got my share of the cheese.

20) The light was shining through the night.

Now practise your letter 'h', by writing out this passage below

Handwriting Heaven's such a happy place,
But Handwriting Hell is a horrid disgrace!

Joining the letter 'h'

h ....

h ....

1) ....

2) ....

3) ....

4) ....

5) ....

6) ....

7) ....

8) ....

9) ....

10) ....

11) ....

12) ....

13) ....

14) ....

15) ....

16) ....

17) ....

18) ....

19) ....

20) ....

Paragraph practice

....

....

Joining the letter "i"

In order to reach Handwriting Heaven, make sure that in [   ] out of 20 of the sentences below, the letter 'i' is written and joined correctly.

1) I'd like to live in a nice icy igloo.

2) I'd drink juice and eat icecream and pizza.

3) I think that kind of life would suit me just fine!

4) The mice in the kitchen steal all the pickles.

5) I tickle my sister to make her grin.

6) When we drive in the car I sit in the middle.

7) Millie used invisible ink in her picture.

8) I picked up the dice and rolled a six.

9) The plastic mice tricked my kitten.

10) I often imagine having millions of pigs.

11) If you get things right, you will get lots of ticks.

12) Getting it right all the time is impossible.

13) Most of the time will be quite impressive.

14) My favourite insects are spiders and earwigs.

15) Alice and Tim climbed onto the fridge.

16) "They spied on me with mirrors," whined Vic.

17) Fairies are little and wear tiny slippers.

18) My Auntie Rita is nice — but dim.

19) My sister's hair is silky, and mine is a mess!

20) Claire fired her air rifle at the evil imps.

Now practise your letter 'i', by writing out this passage below

Handwriting Heaven is fit for a king,
While Handwriting Hell does nothing but ming.

Joining the letter "i"

i ....
i ....

1) ....
2) ....
3) ....
4) ....
5) ....
6) ....
7) ....
8) ....
9) ....
10) ....
11) ....
12) ....
13) ....
14) ....
15) ....
16) ....
17) ....
18) ....
19) ....
20) ....

Paragraph practice

....
....

Joining the letter 'j'

In order to reach Handwriting Heaven, make sure that in ☐ out of 20 of the sentences below, the letter 'j' is written and joined correctly.

1) The jockey jumped for joy when he won.

2) These jeans go just right with my new jumper.

3) "Jingle bells, jingle bells," sang the choir.

4) I hide my jewellery in a jam jar on journeys.

5) If somebody steals it, they might go to jail.

6) "Justice will be done," promised the judge.

7) I told so many jokes that my jaw was aching.

8) In America they call jam, 'jelly'.

9) Don't know what they call jelly — maybe jam!

10) Jenny and I came joint second in long jump.

11) "Just my luck," said the jolly juggler.

12) Princess Jasmine wears jewelled pyjamas.

13) Uncle Joe is the janitor at my junior school.

14) "Don't be so juvenile," jeered my big sister.

15) The jagged piece of jigsaw joined just right.

16) Jane gave the jackal a jug of juice.

17) I know some jellyfish that do Judo and jogging.

18) Mr Majika adjusted his glasses.

19) He gave me the injection — what a jab!

20) Dad's new Jaguar caused the traffic jam.

Now practise your letter 'j', by writing out this passage below

It's just so hard to adjust to Handwriting Hell,

It's partly the jagged edges, but mainly the smell.

Joining the letter "j"

j ....

j ....

1) ....

2) ....

3) ....

4) ....

5) ....

6) ....

7) ....

8) ....

9) ....

10) ....

11) ....

12) ....

13) ....

14) ....

15) ....

16) ....

17) ....

18) ....

19) ....

20) ....

Paragraph practice

....

....

Joining the letter 'k'

In order to reach Handwriting Heaven, make sure that in ☐ out of 20 of the sentences below, the letter 'k' is written and joined correctly.

1) Zack pricked his finger on a knitting needle.

2) I stuck a cork in my kettle to catch the genie.

3) A mean trick — but I wanted to make a wish!

4) I wished to be king, but all I got was a smack.

5) I keep my gym kit in my backpack.

6) Mike cooked baked bean pie — it stank.

7) I crack my knuckles, but I don't pick my nose.

8) The kids chuckled when dad fell in the lake.

9) He was chasing a kite, and fell over a plank.

10) I was locked out for ages when I lost my key.

11) Don't tell jokes to koalas — they might attack.

12) I keep on snacking on crackers and cake.

13) Kicking donkeys is not kind.

14) Ken chucked a stick for his dog to fetch back.

15) A burning haystack makes thick black smoke.

16) The knight walked meekly up to the kiosk.

17) The knock at the door jerked me awake.

18) The unlucky lumberjack broke his knee.

19) Knitting's not hard — but there's a knack to it.

20) "You're making a mistake," warned the duck.

Now practise your letter 'k', by writing out this passage below

Don't worry if you get stuck, or if you make mistakes,
Handwriting Heaven's waiting — practice is all it takes.

Joining the letter 'k'

k ....

k ....

1) ....

2) ....

3) ....

4) ....

5) ....

6) ....

7) ....

8) ....

9) ....

10) ....

11) ....

12) ....

13) ....

14) ....

15) ....

16) ....

17) ....

18) ....

19) ....

20) ....

Paragraph practice

....

....

Joining the letter 'l'

In order to reach Handwriting Heaven, make sure that in ▮ out of 20 of the sentences below, the letter 'l' is written and joined correctly.

1) Lilly licked a lollipop, then launched it at Lila!

2) The little lamb wobbled as it walked.

3) The unruly footballer lunged at the linesman.

4) In the middle of July we get glorious weather.

5) A lady called Jill kindly cleaned my pullover.

6) "Listen and you'll learn lots," I exclaimed.

7) I blew up the balloon until it was full.

8) Then a little bit more — what an explosion!

9) The large bull was rolling down the hill.

10) My elf is too small to hear when I call him.

11) It's really silly to go sailing without a life belt.

12) My lion has fallen out of my lorry.

13) At lunchtime I like to leave lettuce alone.

14) "My legs are too long," said Bill slowly.

15) The clever girl could talk in eleven languages.

16) My lovely labrador likes his old collar.

17) Juliet leaned lazily over the balcony.

18) Smiling and laughing helps me feel cheerful.

19) Polly unplugged the lamp and left the lounge.

20) Lilies are flowers that smell delightful.

Now practise your letter 'l', by writing out this passage below

Handwriting Heaven's a little hard to believe,

But I'll tell you this — you won't want to leave.

Joining the letter 'l'

l
....

l
....

1) ....

2) ....

3) ....

4) ....

5) ....

6) ....

7) ....

8) ....

9) ....

10) ....

11) ....

12) ....

13) ....

14) ....

15) ....

16) ....

17) ....

18) ....

19) ....

20) ....

Paragraph practice

....

....

Joining the letter 'm'

In order to reach Handwriting Heaven, make sure that in ☐ out of 20 of the sentences below, the letter 'm' is written and joined correctly.

1) "Mummy! Mummy!" screamed baby Simon.

2) I can't help mumbling — my mouth's small.

3) Maths homework makes me mad sometimes.

4) My mum's pet lemming is sad at the moment.

5) He may be miserable until she comes home.

6) Poor Adam hit his thumb with a hammer.

7) I dreamed I combed a monkey's moustache.

8) My team fumed at the mention of a re-match.

9) I must remember to milk cows more often.

10) Mystical magicians make mounds of magic.

11) Pumas — majestic members of the cat family.

12) I tumbled over and bumped my bum!

13) Pamela smiled, mixing melon with marmite.

14) Many monsters might seem meek and mild.

15) In summer I make more time for my music.

16) It's more tricky to hum with a mouthful of jam.

17) My mate Emma makes up amazing poems.

18) Mum makes marvellous scrambled egg.

19) Sam's tummy rumbled — almost mealtime.

20) My mop made muddy marks on the mat.

Now practise your letter 'm', by writing out this passage below

If I say "marvellous, magnificent, supreme,"
I bet you can guess which of the places I mean.

Joining the letter 'm'

m ....

m ....

1) ....

2) ....

3) ....

4) ....

5) ....

6) ....

7) ....

8) ....

9) ....

10) ....

11) ....

12) ....

13) ....

14) ....

15) ....

16) ....

17) ....

18) ....

19) ....

20) ....

Paragraph practice

....

....

Joining the letter 'n'

In order to reach Handwriting Heaven, make sure that in ☐ out of 20 of the sentences below, the letter 'n' is written and joined correctly.

1) Fran learned one new song on Monday.

2) But the next night she'd nearly forgotten it.

3) "Not good enough," moaned her instructor.

4) I found it funny when Janet danced the can-can.

5) The noisy skunk was named Nancy.

6) She had a certain scent that was a bit nasty.

7) I often fancy bacon and beans for dinner.

8) Ronnie pinned a pinecone to his pants.

9) I wanted to win but ended up coming ninth.

10) Danny planned a brilliant prank.

11) Stan hadn't seen many martians until then.

12) Suddenly, he was surrounded by millions.

13) But they hadn't meant to sneak up on him.

14) In fact they were friendly and knew his name.

15) I often pretend this pan is a handbag.

16) Annie is banned from opening tins.

17) She never notices when they're upside down.

18) When I'm naughty, nice things never happen.

19) Jenny's boyfriend is so nice and romantic.

20) On Valentine's day, her present was a bin!

Now practise your letter 'n', by writing out this passage below

If I say, "this place is nasty and noisy, let me out!"
I'm certain you know where I'm moaning about.

Joining the letter 'n'

n ....

n ....

1) ....

2) ....

3) ....

4) ....

5) ....

6) ....

7) ....

8) ....

9) ....

10) ....

11) ....

12) ....

13) ....

14) ....

15) ....

16) ....

17) ....

18) ....

19) ....

20) ....

Paragraph practice

....

....

Joining the letter 'o'

In order to reach Handwriting Heaven, make sure that in ☐ out of 20 of the sentences below, the letter 'o' is written and joined correctly.

1) Ollie's too short to open the door.

2) My school can be boring, but mostly it's good.

3) I told my cow I understood her problem.

4) As soon as it got cold, I lost my gloves.

5) Nobody knows why goats don't have toes.

6) Everyone knows they don't like toads.

7) "Oh no! Our power's off!" howled the editors.

8) Jo and I both fit in Aunt Molly's bloomers.

9) My brother's one, and he's got one tooth too.

10) Rolo the octopus would love some hot cocoa.

11) Baboons and orangutans took over my pool.

12) My boots are made for plodding — slowly.

13) I stood on a stool to close the open window.

14) Most plants have flowers, roots and shoots.

15) There's a moose loose in our orchard.

16) I play snooker with lemons and oranges.

17) I cooked potato and tomato soup.

18) Modern songs soothe my soul more than old.

19) I followed Polly down to the toolshed.

20) She used her toolbox to fix my broken spoon.

Now practise your letter 'o', by writing out this passage below

As you know, Handwriting Hell is no bed of roses,
Please, if you've to go down there, do hold your noses.

Joining the letter 'o'

o ....

o ....

1) ....

2) ....

3) ....

4) ....

5) ....

6) ....

7) ....

8) ....

9) ....

10) ....

11) ....

12) ....

13) ....

14) ....

15) ....

16) ....

17) ....

18) ....

19) ....

20) ....

Paragraph practice

....

....

Joining the letter 'p'

In order to reach Handwriting Heaven, make sure that in [ ] out of 20 of the sentences below, the letter 'p' is written and joined correctly.

1) Copper pots look pretty when polished up.

2) The policeman pursued the pick-pocket.

3) I hope I keep hopping when I go shopping.

4) Pumpkin prices are cheap in September.

5) My pig can play the piano and harp.

6) The spotted puppy's name was Poppy.

7) Put pepper in your pasta to make it spicy.

8) I pricked my palm picking up a sharp pebble.

9) Bagpipe practice keeps me up all night.

10) The ship plowed through the deep Pacific.

11) Some people panic when put on a pony.

12) Peggy keeps her parlour spick and span.

13) Porcupines have prickly spines.

14) The slippery spy spotted the priceless picture.

15) Rupert tripped skipping and ripped his pants.

16) I pity the sprinter who was pipped at the post.

17) "This is pretty poor porridge," spat Pippa.

18) Spiteful pirates push prisoners off planks.

19) The spider rapidly spun a parachute.

20) Flipper the porpoise prefers parties to sleep.

Now practise your letter 'p', by writing out this passage below

You know, Handwriting Heaven would be perfect for you,
But Handwriting Hell is a big pile of poo.

Joining the letter 'p'

p ....

p ....

1) ....

2) ....

3) ....

4) ....

5) ....

6) ....

7) ....

8) ....

9) ....

10) ....

11) ....

12) ....

13) ....

14) ....

15) ....

16) ....

17) ....

18) ....

19) ....

20) ....

Paragraph practice

....

....

Joining the letter 'r'

In order to reach Handwriting Heaven, make sure that in [ ] out of 20 of the sentences below, the letter 'r' is written and joined correctly.

1) Fergus frowned at Freda as she fried the rat.

2) "Pardon my French," burped the Baron.

3) The cart full of carrots rattled down the track.

4) My brain was hurting from all the hard work.

5) I was sorry I'd gone running when it rained.

6) I stared at my bright red bedroom in horror.

7) My rotten brother had redecorated it!

8) But I'll get my revenge — don't you worry.

9) Raspberries are my rabbit's favourite fruit.

10) My project on Portugal scored high marks.

11) The jumper's price was reduced — bargain!

12) The rubies and emeralds sparkled brightly.

13) Carrie's hair is brown and Ernie's is ginger.

14) The travellers rushed along the rope bridge.

15) It's great exploring foreign countries.

16) "My real name is Margarita Carmen," she said.

17) I tried very hard to train my tiger.

18) But I really wouldn't recommend it to a friend.

19) I'd rather raise rabbits from now on.

20) The Prince and Princess argued all winter.

Now practise your letter 'r', by writing out this passage below

You won't rate the breakfasts in Handwriting Hell,
Roasted rats' livers — which is dinner as well.

Joining the letter 'r'

r ....

r ....

1) ....

2) ....

3) ....

4) ....

5) ....

6) ....

7) ....

8) ....

9) ....

10) ....

11) ....

12) ....

13) ....

14) ....

15) ....

16) ....

17) ....

18) ....

19) ....

20) ....

Paragraph practice

....

....

Joining the letters 's' and 't'

In order to reach Handwriting Heaven, make sure that in [ ] out of 20 of the sentences below, the letters 's' and 't' are written and joined correctly.

1) My sister whistles the stupidest songs.

2) In summer the sunshine keeps me smiling.

3) Miss Moss fusses lots, but she's still sweet.

4) Snails and slugs are seriously slimy things.

5) Jess was bruised as she slid down the slide.

6) Sam sat in the saddle of the strong stallion.

7) I like splashing in the sea at the sandy shore.

8) Sausages at breakfast stop me oversleeping.

9) The smelly dogs sat sadly in the sink.

10) The sneaky, sneering cat sniggered.

11) The tiny tarantula tiptoed timidly past.

12) I got first turn at batting in cricket practice.

13) The only way to get better at it is to try.

14) Betty is bitter about getting sent out to town.

15) My little brothers are called the terrible twins.

16) My big brother's a teenager with a temper!

17) I'm not the best at untying tight knots.

18) The title of the text book terrified me.

19) The two tortoises talked all through the night.

20) Twenty tawny tigers trotted through the town.

Now practise your letters 's' and 't', by writing out this passage below

It's stunning, it's staggering, it's simply the best,
Handwriting Heaven outshines all the rest.

Joining the letters 's' and 't'

s ....

t ....

1) ....

2) ....

3) ....

4) ....

5) ....

6) ....

7) ....

8) ....

9) ....

10) ....

11) ....

12) ....

13) ....

14) ....

15) ....

16) ....

17) ....

18) ....

19) ....

20) ....

Paragraph practice

....

....

Joining the letter 'u'

In order to reach Handwriting Heaven, make sure that in [ ] out of 20 of the sentences below, the letter 'u' is written and joined correctly.

1) I think the umbrella's under the cupboard.

2) If you mutter and mumble you'll never be loud.

3) Shout up if you don't fully understand.

4) Julie found a bug in her burger — yuk!

5) It was unlucky the duvet got burnt in the sun.

6) The duck got mucky in the muddy puddle.

7) My bunny's a bundle of fluff that liked cuddles.

8) Trudy liked the sound of the mountain.

9) If I feel proud, I shout it aloud — to the clouds!

10) The baby in a buggy sucked a rubber dummy.

11) Too many plums make my gums numb.

12) The plump drummer thumped his drum loudly.

13) The huge truck bumped into the old hut.

14) Where did that squirrel put his nuts?

15) Somewhere about, but they couldn't be found.

16) You can have lots of fun with a buttered bun.

17) Ursula jumped up with a bound.

18) Sue stuck her thumb in mum's apple crumble.

19) I pushed, I pulled, but the cub wouldn't budge.

20) For pudding Doug ate four pounds of fudge.

Now practise your letter 'u', by writing out this passage below

It's no bundle of fun here, and that's for sure,
I'm in Handwriting Hell — wishing I'd practised more.

u ....

u ....

1) ....

2) ....

3) ....

4) ....

5) ....

6) ....

7) ....

8) ....

9) ....

10) ....

11) ....

12) ....

13) ....

14) ....

15) ....

16) ....

17) ....

18) ....

19) ....

20) ....

Paragraph practice

....

....

Joining the letters 'v' and 'w'

In order to reach Handwriting Heaven, make sure that in ☐ out of 20 of the sentences below, the letters 'v' and 'w' are written and joined correctly.

1) Vases look lovely when they have violets in.

2) They're also very nice when covered in voles.

3) However, some voles behave quite violently.

4) And if they get vicious, the vase won't survive.

5) I attacked the various vegetables with knives.

6) Kevin loves varnishing olives and vines.

7) The whole village had vanished overnight.

8) The goalkeeper bravely dived to save it.

9) Steve favours videos over television.

10) Very little point having chips without vinegar.

11) The whistle went, so we wandered away.

12) The waiter walked over with the white wine.

13) The witch was wrinkled and had whiskers.

14) Why, oh why, is my waist so wobbly?

15) We watched the walrus chewing flowers.

16) Wise minnows are few and far between.

17) I'm wary when walking through the woods.

18) I wolfed down the wonderful bowl of stew.

19) The wailing wind woke up the twins.

20) The swan waved its wing in a last farewell.

Now practise your letters 'v' and 'w', by writing out this passage below

In Handwriting Heaven we're all wonderful and wise,
So strive to join us here, that's what I advise.

Joining the letters 'v' and 'w'

v ....

w ....

1) ....

2) ....

3) ....

4) ....

5) ....

6) ....

7) ....

8) ....

9) ....

10) ....

11) ....

12) ....

13) ....

14) ....

15) ....

16) ....

17) ....

18) ....

19) ....

20) ....

Paragraph practice

....

....

Joining the letters 'q' and 'x'

In order to reach Handwriting Heaven, make sure that in [ ] out of 20 of the sentences below, the letters 'q' and 'x' are written and joined correctly.

1) Sequins covered the beauty queen's gown.

2) The sequence of events was quite confusing.

3) Guests at banquets aren't usually this quiet.

4) The quarrelling ducks quacked angrily.

5) Max hoped his team would equalise quickly.

6) I frequently forget how squashed your face is.

7) The quality of the quiche was quite excellent.

8) He quenched his thirst with lemon squash.

9) I had no qualms about jumping the queue.

10) A quarter of Zara's work was just squiggles.

11) Alex got the maximum marks in his exam.

12) I couldn't coax the fox into my garden.

13) I expect Wales exports a lot of sheep.

14) Max's explanation was extraordinary.

15) Oh no — the fax machine's exploded.

16) The tax man maximised my expenses.

17) Muhammad Ali was an expert at boxing.

18) I wonder if extra-terrestrials really exist.

19) The pixie fixed it so that my arms extended.

20) Now I can stir the mixture from further away.

Now practise your letters 'q' and 'x', by writing out this passage below

I'm excited by the quality of Handwriting Heaven.
I'll request to stay an extra month, or possibly forever.

q ....

x ....

1) ....

2) ....

3) ....

4) ....

5) ....

6) ....

7) ....

8) ....

9) ....

10) ....

11) ....

12) ....

13) ....

14) ....

15) ....

16) ....

17) ....

18) ....

19) ....

20) ....

Paragraph practice

....

....

Joining the letters 'y' and 'z'

In order to reach Handwriting Heaven, make sure that in [ ] out of 20 of the sentences below, the letters 'y' and 'z' are written and joined correctly.

1) Our balcony is absolutely lovely.

2) It's twenty yards long and painted yellow.

3) The boys stayed in the yard all day.

4) They were very thirsty but they played on.

5) "Why do you get a say?" asked Jay angrily.

6) But the pony, not surprisingly, didn't reply.

7) There's no way I'd pay for your yoghurt today.

8) Even if you'd asked yesterday, it'd be unlikely.

9) The smelly baby Yeti was lying in Sally's way.

10) Yvonne's been yelling at me for nearly a year.

11) Fizzy drinks always make me dizzy.

12) Zebras zig-zagged across the office.

13) The crazy cowboy amazed the crowd.

14) I was dazzled by the blazing comet.

15) The puzzle was so boring it made me doze.

16) Don't be fazed by the haze around my head.

17) Zookeepers often get lost in mazes.

18) My latest craze is zooming down the banister.

19) The breeze blew up the back of my blazer.

20) I was dazed by Zoe's brazen behaviour.

Now practise your letters 'y' and 'z', by writing out this passage below

I've said it twenty times, and I'll say it all day,
Handwriting Heaven's dazzling, and it's not far away.